Little Book of
Elves &
Fairies

Little Book of
Elves &
Fairies

Illustrations by
Ida Rentoul Outhwaite

Buster Books

Contents

What is a Fairy?	6
Believe in Fairies: ANON	8
House Brownies	10
Elves & Pixies	12
Being Pixy-led	15
Daisies: FRANK DEMPSTER SHERMAN	17
Dwarfs, Gnomes and Goblins	18
Stolen Humans	21
Changelings	24

Goblin Market [extract]:
   CHRISTINA ROSSETTI 27

Lady of Llyn y Fan Fach 30

Queen Mab: THOMAS HOOD 32

Fairy Godmothers 35

About the Fairies: JEAN INGELOW 36

Fairy Animals 38

Rainbow Fairies: ANON 41

'Horse and Hattock' 42

The Fairies: SYBIL MORFORD 44

Fairy Trees 46

Mermaids & Nixies 49

Do you seek the road to Fairyland?:
   ERNEST THOMPSON SETON 50

Young Tam Lyn 53

Oh! where do fairies hide their heads?:
   THOMAS HAYNES BAYLY 56

Seeing Fairies 58

I Believe: FELICIA D. BROWNE-HEMANS 60

A Spell to see Fairies 62

What is a Fairy?

Fairies have added mystery and delight to stories for hundreds of years. Whether they are tall, beautiful and kindly, like the peris described in TALES OF THE ARABIAN NIGHTS, or small, homely and mischievous hobs, goblins and house brownies, these magical creatures appear in stories from all over Europe.

Tinkerbell, in PETER PAN AND WENDY, has many ancestors. William Shakespeare described the Fairy Queen, Mab, as being no bigger than the gemstone in a ring, so we can be sure that people have believed in these tiny beings for at least 400 years.

Fairies first appeared in French stories in the 1780s. Many of our favourite fairy tales – such as CINDERELLA, SLEEPING BEAUTY or BEAUTY AND THE BEAST – were written at that time. They describe unearthly beings that range from beautiful, young nymphs to ugly and tetchy fairy godmothers.

The behaviour of fairies varies from story to story. Sometimes they help hapless princes, punish naughty children and reward the good; but sometimes they are much more dangerous to the humans who crossed their path, as you will discover....

Believe in Fairies

Believe in the Fairies
Who make dreams come true.
Believe in the wonder,
The stars and the moon.
Believe in the magic,
From Fairies above.
They dance on the flowers,
And sing songs of love.
And if you just believe,
And always stay true,
The Fairies will be there,
To watch over you!

ANON

House Brownies

Brownies are always described as being hairy, naked and are attached to one farm or family. They are seldom seen unless they want to be. They tend the cows and sheep, clean the house, look after the farm buildings, and generally work so that the property or family thrives.

Sadly, sometimes brownies turn bad and become a real nuisance. They overturn churns and spoil the butter, open gates so that the animals can escape, drop nests down kitchen chimneys so that stoves smoke and won't cook, and generally become as destructive as they were helpful before.

There is a story about a Yorkshire farmer who was so plagued by a bad brownie that he decided to leave his farm. He packed all his possession into waggons and had just pulled out of the farmyard, when he met a neighbour.

'Are you flitting?' asked the neighbour.

'Aye' said the farmer.

'Aye' said the brownie, popping his head out of one of the waggons, 'we're flitting.'

'What?' said the farmer, looking outraged. 'If you're coming with me, I'm not going!'

And he turned the waggons round and went back to his farm.

The story doesn't tell if the brownie behaved better after this, but maybe the farmer decided to 'lay' him instead. It is very easy to do this.

All you have to do is to make the brownie a suit of
clothes. As soon as he puts them on, he is released
from the tie that binds him to a farm or family.

Elves and Pixies

Stories about elves are found all over Europe. In Scandinavia, there were Light Elves, who lived above ground, and Dark Elves, who lived underground and only came out at night. Dark Elves were unfriendly, but Light Elves came to human gatherings and sometimes married even humans. The only way they could be identified was by their tails.

One story tells how a man was dancing with a Light Elf girl when he noticed her tail showing under her dress. Rather than shame her, he whispered, 'Forgive me, lady, but your garter is slipping.' Because of his politeness, she blessed him and he had good luck for the rest of his life.

The pixies were the elves of the West Country. They were known as piskies in Cornwall. They had red hair, turned up noses, and dressed in green. Pixies could be very cruel to humans who were rude or unkind to others. There are many stories of them leading such people into bogs or playing tricks on them.

Pixies would borrow horses to travel around, riding anything up to 20 on one horse. Any horse found sweating in its stall in the morning was described as 'pixy-ridden'.

Being Pixy-led

Many parts of Europe have stories of travellers who are led astray, or 'pixy-led', by mischievous fairies. Some fairies seem to do it for amusement, but others have a more sinister motive. They lead unwary travellers away from safe paths into bogs or other hazards.

A Will o' the Wisp is sometimes said to be the soul of an evil man, who has been banned from both Heaven and Hell and must roam the Earth as a fairy with only a burning coal for warmth. In revenge, he lures unwary travellers to their doom with his light. They believe they are walking towards the light of a house, but find only a watery death.

Another common misleader is Robin Goodfellow, otherwise known as Puck (who appears in Shakespeare's play A Midsummer's Night's Dream). He is a practical joker, who distracts travellers from their road, but does not lead them into danger.

Cornish stories tell of pixies who would lead people astray by casting a thick mist around them. They could not see where they were going and would simply walk endlessly in circles.

To rescue someone who has been pixy-led, it is sometimes enough to whistle, to wear hob-nailed boots, or to carry salt in your pocket (because iron and salt both destroy magic). But the best way is to turn a victim's coat inside out – then the mist will vanish instantly.

Daisies

At evening when I go to bed
I see the stars shine overhead;
They are the little daisies white
That dot the meadow of the night.

And often while I'm dreaming so,
Across the sky the moon will go;
It is a lady, sweet and fair,
Who comes to gather daisies there.

For, when at morning I arise,
There's not a star left in the skies;
She's picked them all and dropped them down
Into the meadows of the town.

FRANK DEMPSTER SHERMAN

Dwarves, Gnomes and Goblins

Dwarves are mostly found in German and Swiss stories. They are small, only about a meter tall, and can be identified by their long beards. They work in mines, digging for gems and precious metals. Dwarves are exceptionally skilled in metalworking and make the most beautiful things, which are often magical. They usually live in caves or in holes under the ground. They can be hostile towards to humans, but can also perform small tasks for them. They are believed to steal babies and children, leaving changelings (see page 24) in their place.

Gnomes are a race of small, misshapen, dwarf-like creatures that live underground, where they guard their treasures. They can move as easily through the solid earth as humans walk upon it. They cannot stand the light of the sun, and even one sunbeam would turn them into stone. Gnomes avoid humans, but miners can sometimes hear them knocking deep down in the mines.

Stories of goblins originated in south-western France, but spread rapidly all over Europe. Goblins usually live in caves or in hollows within the roots of ancient trees, although they never stay anywhere very long. They are a different, more grotesque variety of gnomes. They can be playful, but are often evil and their tricks can seriously harm people. They pester humans in a number of ways, such as hiding small objects, tipping over pails of milk and turning signposts around.

Stolen Humans

Most of what we know about fairies seems to come from the stories of people who have visited fairy worlds. This happens either when the person is invited or is captured because they have broken a fairy law. Those who manage to escape a fairy world can take years to recover and may die young.

Fairies are particularly interested in stealing new-born babies, nursing mothers, beautiful young women, and young men who are gifted in music and song. Stories tell how nursing mothers are used as 'wet-nurses' – they would have to give their milk to a fairy child whose fairy mother had none.

There are various ways to rescue someone from the fairies. One way is described in the ballad Young Tam Lin (see page 52). Another is described in this story of a blacksmith who saved his son from the fairies in Western Scotland:

There was once a blacksmith who had only one son. When the son was about 14 years old, he strayed on to a fairy knowe [mound] and was captured by the fairies. They sent a changeling (see page 24) back to his father. However the smith soon detected the fraud and got rid of the changeling. Unfortunately the fairies did not release the boy, and so the smith had to go and rescue his son himself.

The smith went to visit a 'cunning man', who was reputed to know a lot about the fairies and their ways. The cunning man advised the smith on what to do and said he must wait until Beltane [1 May] when the fairy knowes open. The smith went home again and waited patiently for the day to come.

On the evening of Beltane, the smith collected a bible, an iron knife and a cock which he put in a sack. Then he went to the knowe and waited. At midnight, the knowe opened. A bright light shone from it and he heard music and laughter.

Quickly the smith drove the knife into the side of the opening, and then pulled the cock out of the sack. The cock saw the bright light and thought it was the dawn, so he started crowing vigorously. At once the knowe began to close, but the iron knife prevented it from closing completely. Screams and shouts came from the opening, and the fairies came rushing out to defend their kingdom against whoever was attacking them. They saw the smith and swooped on him, but he followed the cunning man's instructions and put the bible over his head. The fairies could not touch him.

'All I want is my son!' he shouted to them. 'Give him back and I will remove my knife at once.'

'Bring the boy! Bring the boy!' cried the fairies. There was a whoosh and the boy lay unconscious on the grass. The smith pulled his knife out of the side of the opening, which immediately slammed shut. The smith grabbed his son and sprinted home.

The next day he sent for the parson, who sprinkled the unconscious boy with holy water. Then the boy opened his eyes, sat up in bed and kissed his father. Fortunately, the boy did not pine or become sick from his experience and, because the fairies had taught him much about smithying, he became the best blacksmith in all of Scotland.

Changelings

Changelings are creatures left by fairies in the place of a stolen child to try to convince the real parents that their child has not disappeared. A changeling may be carved from a log, or a fairy child left instead of the human child.

One story tells of how a mother found that her baby had been replaced by a changeling. She was weeping for her lost child, when suddenly the door opened. A strange woman came in and snatched the changeling out of the cradle.

'They stole your child for me,' she said, 'but I prefer my own son!' She strode out of the room, and then the mother heard crying outside. Rushing out, she found her own baby, safe and sound.

Sometimes fairies send a very old fairy to replace a human toddler with a changeling. To detect this kind of changeling, the mother, or sometimes a wise woman, had to take 24 eggshells, set them up on the hearth, and start to brew beer. The changeling would sit up in its bed or chair and declare: 'I heard it from my father, and he from his, and he from his, that an acorn was before the oak, and the oak was in the ground, but I have never seen brewing done in eggshells before!'

Once the mother knew that the toddler was a changeling, she had to heat a shovel until it was red-hot, then hold the child above it and let it fall. The changeling would fly away up the chimney, laughing or shrieking, and her child would be returned safe and sound.

Goblin Market
[extract]

Backwards up the mossy glen
Turn'd and troop'd the goblin men,
With their shrill repeated cry,
'Come buy, come buy.'
When they reach'd where Laura was
They stood stock still upon the moss,
Leering at each other,
Brother with sly brother.
One set his basket down,
One rear'd his plate;
One began to weave a crown
Of tendrils, leaves, and rough nuts brown
(Men sell not such in any town);
One heav'd the golden weight
Of dish and fruit to offer her:
'Come buy, come buy,' was still their cry.
Laura stared but did not stir,
Long'd but had no money:
The whisk-tail'd merchant bade her taste
In tones as smooth as honey,
The cat-faced purr'd,
The rat-faced spoke a word
Of welcome, and the snail-paced
Even was heard.

But sweet-tooth Laura spoke in haste:
'Good folk, I have no coin;
To take were to purloin:
I have no copper in my purse,
I have no silver either,
And all my gold is on the furze
That shakes in windy weather
Above the rusty heather.'
'You have much gold upon your head,'
They answer'd all together:
'Buy from us with a golden curl.'
She clipp'd a precious golden lock,
She dropp'd a tear more rare than pearl,
Then suck'd their fruit globes fair or red:
Sweeter than honey from the rock,
Stronger than man-rejoicing wine,
Clearer than water flow'd that juice;
She never tasted such before,
How should it cloy with length of use?
She suck'd and suck'd and suck'd the more
Fruits which that unknown orchard bore;
She suck'd until her lips were sore;
Then flung the emptied rinds away
But gather'd up one kernel stone,
And knew not was it night or day
As she turn'd home alone.

Lizzie met her at the gate
Full of wise upbraidings:
'Dear, you should not stay so late,
Twilight is not good for maidens;
Should not loiter in the glen
In the haunts of goblin men.
Do you not remember Jeanie,
How she met them in the moonlight,
Took their gifts both choice and many,
Ate their fruits and wore their flowers
Pluck'd from bowers
Where summer ripens at all hours?
But ever in the noonlight
She pined and pined away;
Sought them by night and day,
Found them no more,
but dwindled and grew grey;
Then fell with the first snow,
While to this day no grass will grow
Where she lies low:
I planted daisies there a year ago
That never blow.
You should not loiter so.'

CHRISTINA ROSSETTI

The Lady of Llan y Fan Fach

There was once a farmer who grazed his cattle beside Fan Fach lake in Wales. One day he saw a beautiful woman sitting on the surface of the lake combing her long golden hair. Instantly, he fell in love with her. Her father only agreed to their marriage after the farmer had identified her from among her sisters by the way her sandals were laced. Her marriage dowry was a herd of magical cows which gave three times the milk of any normal cow. However, her father warned him that if he struck her three times, she would leave him for ever.

They lived happily for several years and had three sons, but sometimes the wife behaved oddly. She wept at weddings and laughed at funerals. On three separate occasions, her husband couldn't resist tapping her on the shoulder. On the third time, she cried bitterly and then vanished into the lake. She was followed by her cows and all their descendants, 'even a slaughtered calf hanging in the larder'.

She never returned to her husband but would visit her sons from time to time. She taught them many remedies against sickness, so that they became successful doctors whose fame spread far and wide.

In some versions of this story, the husband finds his wife's swan-feather robe, or her seal skin, and hides it. The wife stays on earth until she can retrieve her magical garment. Only then she can transform herself and depart.

Queen Mab

A little fairy comes at night,
Her eyes are blue, her hair is brown,
With silver spots upon her wings,
And from the moon she flutters down.

She has a little silver wand,
And when a good child goes to bed
She waves her hand from right to left,
And makes a circle round its head.

And then it dreams of pleasant things,
Of fountains filled with fairy fish,
And trees that bear delicious fruit,
And bow their branches at a wish:

And talking birds with gifted tongues,
For singing songs and telling tales,
And pretty dwarfs to show the way
Through fairy hills and fairy dales.

But when a bad child goes to bed,
From left to right she weaves her rings,
And then it dreams all through the night
Of only ugly horrid things!

Then stormy waves rush on to drown,
Or raging flames come scorching round,
Fierce dragons hover in the air,
And serpents crawl along the ground.

Then wicked children wake and weep,
And wish the long black gloom away;
But good ones love the dark, and find
The night as pleasant as the day.

THOMAS HOOD

Fairy Godmothers

Fairy godmothers first appeared in French fairy tales during the eighteenth century. Before this, fairies across Europe had helped people who were kind, generous, polite, clean and tidy, but they did not interfere with humans except when humans stumbled across the fairy kingdoms.

French fairy godmothers, on the other hand, seem to made a decision to improve their godchildren generally. For example, in Beauty and the Beast, a prince is transformed by his fairy godmother because of his selfishness and temper tantrums. Sometimes a fairy godmother removed a prince or princess from their family and brought them up in her palace because she disapproved of their parents' foolishness or cruelty.

However, fairy godmothers never seem to be around when they are needed. Cinderella's only turns up after her stepmother has reduced her to a servant. Sleeping Beauty's six godmothers could not protect her from pricking her finger on a spindle. Having a fairy godmother was not necessarily an advantage!

And, have you noticed, there are no fairy godfathers? When a prince is said to have a godfather, he was always a magician with great powers, but he is a human. So, if there are no fairy godfathers, where do fairy godmothers come from?

About the Fairies

Pray, where are the little bluebells gone,
That lately blossomed in the wood?
Why, the fairies have each taken one,
And put it on for a hood.

And where are the pretty grass-stalks gone,
That waved in the summer breeze?
Oh, the fairies have taken them, every one,
To plant in their gardens like trees.

And where are the great big blue-bottles gone,
That buzzed in their busy pride?
Oh, the fairies have caught them, every one,
And have broken them in to ride.

And they've taken the glow-worms to light
their halls,
And the cricket to sing them a song;
And the great red rose leaves to paper their walls,
And they're feasting the whole night long.

And when Spring comes back, with its
mild soft ray,
And the ripple of gentle rain,
The fairies bring what they've taken away,
And give it us all again.

JEAN INGELOW

Fairy Animals

Fairy godmothers use many different animals and birds as messengers, as assistants, and to pull their chariots. We hear of chariots pulled by butterflies, doves, peacocks and dragon-flies among others. Wicked fairy godmothers, on the other hand, usually employ winged serpents, dragons or other dangerous animals.

Fairies often like to punish people by turning them into animals. One prince was turned into a frog, only to be rescued by a princess's kiss. Another prince was turned into a bear by an evil dwarf. A rude and ungrateful girl was enchanted so that every time she spoke, toads and snakes dropped from her lips. In another story, a stream is enchanted so that anyone who drinks from it is transformed into a stag or a deer.

There are also some animals that are part of Fairyland. One of the scariest of these is a fairy horse, sometimes called a phouka or kelpie. It would appear to children near a lake or river in the form of a charming little horse. If they tried to ride it, its back would lengthen until all the children could mount.

Then the kelpie would gallop into the river and disappear beneath the water. Any of the children who tried to dismount, would find they were stuck to the kelpie's back. Most people believed that the kelpie ate its unfortunate captives.

Fairies also breed hounds for hunting deer. These dogs can be identified because they are white all over except for their ears, which are red. A pair of these hounds was occasionally given to a human favoured by the fairies. Our ancestors prized dogs that they thought were fairy gifts highly, as they were always the best hunters and led the pack.

40

The Rainbow Fairies

Two little clouds, one summer's day,
Went flying through the sky;
They went so fast they bumped their heads,
And both began to cry.

Old Father Sun looked out and said:
'Oh, never mind, my dears,
I'll send my little fairy folk
To dry your falling tears.'

One fairy came in violet,
And one wore indigo;
In blue, green, yellow, orange, red,
They made a pretty row.

They wiped the cloud-tears all away,
And then from out the sky,
Upon a line the sunbeams made,
They hung their gowns to dry.

ANON

'Horse and Hattock'

Although they are often pictured with wings, fairies are not very good at flying. They prefer to ride on a twig or a stem of ragwort. This is activated by saying the words, 'Horse and Hattock'. .

One evening, many, many years ago, the Laird of Duffus, which lies on the Moray Firth east of Inverness in Scotland, was inspecting his fields one evening when he saw a large cloud of dust approaching. As it whirled past him, he heard a voice from inside it shout 'Horse and Hattock!' Being a brave man, he called out the same words and was instantly snatched into the cloud and whirled away with a troop of fairies.

When the cloud stopped, the fairies told the Laird, 'This is the King of France's cellar. Take this cup and join us as we sample his wines.' The Laird did so, but he drank so much that he fell asleep behind a barrel. And when the fairies departed, he was left behind.

In the morning the Laird was awakened by the Royal Butler, who dragged him before the King of France. The king asked him to explain what he was doing in the cellar. The Laird told his story and showed the king the gold cup that he was still holding. It was of such curious workmanship that the king believed his story and pardoned him. The Laird returned home eventually with the fairy cup and it became a family heirloom.

Fairies

Have you ever heard the tapping
Of the fairy cobbler men,
When the moon is shining brightly
Thro' the branches in the glen?
Have you seen a crew of goblins
In a water-lily boat,
Softly sliding, gently sliding,
'Mid the rushes tall afloat?

Have you seen the sleeping goblins
'Neath the mushrooms on the hills?
Have you heard the rippling music
Of the tiny fairy rills?
Have you seen the looms where spiders
Spin their sparkling silver threads?
Brightly shining and entwining
Round the nodding flower heads?

If you want to see the fairies,
You must visit them at night,
When the silvery stars are gleaming
And the moon is shining bright.
If you make no sound to warn them,
You will see the fairy men
Laughing, singing, harebells ringing
While the moonbeams light the glen.

Sybil Morford

Fairy Trees

Some trees have very close connections with the fairy world. In Ireland, a solitary hawthorn on a hill, or a ring of three hawthorns, was believed to mark the entrance to a 'hollow hill'. Irish fairies, known as the Sidhe (pronounced Shee), lived in magnificent palaces beneath these hollow hills. But woe betide any humans who fell asleep under one of these hawthorns, or who ate fruit from the enchanted orchards that lay within the hollow hills. They would fall into the power of the fairies and would not be able to return to their families for at least seven years, if not much longer.

Some people believed elder trees were places of safety for good fairies when they were attacked by evil spirits or wicked witches. The trees were protected by the fairies against human attack. It was very unlucky to cut a branch from an elder without asking permission from the fairies first.

Willow trees, on the other hand, were thought to be inhabited by unfriendly spirits. There are stories of ancient willows uprooting themselves at night and stalking the paths along riverbanks in search of late travellers. Those who escaped had little doubt of the willow's murderous intentions....

It was also dangerous to fall asleep under an apple tree. One story about King Arthur and his knights tells how Sir Lancelot did just this and fell into the clutches of Morgan Le Fay, the king's mortal enemy. He only escaped from her castle with the help of one of her ladies-in-waiting, who was in love with him.

Mermaids
and Nixies

The most famous mermaid of all was the Lorelei. She sat on a mountainous rock in the Rhine and, using her beauty and the magic of her irresistible song, she lured young men to their deaths on the rocks below. When the son of the Count Palatinate died trying to capture her, the Count swore he would have revenge.

He sent four of his best soldiers to kill her. To guard against her song, they stuffed their ears with wax before climbing the cliffs. When the Lorelei realised what they intended, she tore the pearls out of her hair and threw them into the river far below. Then she called on her father, the Rhine, to save her. A huge wave swept down the river and carried her away.

The soldiers, who had clung to the rock as the wave passed, reported this to the Count. The Lorelei was never seen again, but her rock still stands in the Rhine just north of Koblenz in Germany.

Strictly speaking, the Lorelei was a 'nixie' or water nymph, not a mermaid. True mermaids live in the sea and are said to lure sailors to their death because they are lonely and are seeking company. Mermen live in the deeps of the sea, raising storms and causing shipwrecks, but seldom come ashore.

Do you seek the road to Fairyland?

Do you seek the road to Fairyland.....
I'll tell; it's easy, quite.
Wait till a yellow moon gets up
O'er purple seas by night,
And gilds a shining pathway
That is sparkling diamond bright
Then, if no evil power be nigh
To thwart you, out of spite,
And if you know the very words
To cast a spell of might,
You get upon a thistledown,
And, if the breeze is right,
You sail away to Fairyland
Along this track of light.

ERNEST THOMPSON SETON

Young Tam Lin

This ballad of Young Tam Lin is one of the best known fairy stories of the British Isles. It starts with the King of Scotland warning the ladies of his court not to ride in Carterhaugh Wood. He tells them that it is haunted by 'Young Tam Lin' who forces every maiden who visits the wood to perform a forfeit.

Despite his commands, the king's only daughter, named Janet, rides to the well in the centre of the wood and picks a rose. Tam Lin appears, makes love to her and she conceives a child.

When Janet returns to her father's court, it soon becomes clear what has happened. When the king asks who the father is, Janet replies that the father is not a member of the court, nor indeed a mortal man at all:

If that I go with child, father,
Myself must bear the blame;
There's never a lord about your house
Shall get the bairn's name.

If my love were an earthly knight
As he's an elfin grey,
I wad not give my own true-love
For any lord that you have.

Janet returns to Carterhaugh Wood on Halloween and summons Tam Lin again. She asks him if he is really an elf or a captured human. Tam Lin tells her that he is the grandson of the Duke of Roxbrugh, and that he was captured by the Fairy Queen when he fell from his horse while out hunting. He has been the queen's favourite, but now he is worried that he has been chosen by the fairies as a sacrifice to the devil:

And pleasant is the fairy land
But, an eerie tale to tell,
Ay at the end of seven years
We pay a tiend [tax] to Hell;
I am so fair and full of flesh
I'm feared it be myself.

When Janet asks how she can save him from this awful fate. Tam Lin tells her:

Just at the mirk and midnight hour
The fairy folk will ride
And they that would their true-love win
At Miles Cross they must abide.

He tells Janet that he will be part of the Fairy Ride and that he will be riding a white horse. He tells her that she must pull him off the horse and hold on to him whatever happens. But when he turns into a burning coal, she must throw him into the well nearby and he will be safe.

Janet goes to Miles Cross and waits. At midnight the Fairy Ride passes:

About the middle of the night
She heard the bridles ring;
This lady was as glad at that
As any earthly thing.

First she let the black pass by,
And then she let the brown;
But quickly she ran to the milk-white steed,
And pulled the rider down.

The fairies turn Tam Lin into a newt, an adder, a bear, a lion, a red-hot sword blade, but Janet holds on to him through all. Finally he turns into a burning coal. When she throws the coal into the well, she finds her naked lover in her arms and covers him with her green cloak. The fairies ride away, but the Fairy Queen curses Janet for taking her most handsome knight.

Oh! where do fairies hide their heads?

Oh! where do fairies hide their heads,
When snow lies on the hills,
When frost has spoiled their mossy beds,
And crystallized their rills?
Beneath the moon they cannot trip
In circles o'er the plain;
And draughts of dew they cannot sip,
Till green leaves come again.

Perhaps, in small, blue diving-bells
They plunge beneath the waves,
Inhabiting the wreathed shells
That lie in coral caves.
Perhaps, in red Vesuvius
Carousals they maintain;
And cheer their little spirits thus,
Till green leaves come again.

When they return, there will be mirth
And music in the air.
And fairy wings upon the earth,
And mischief everywhere.

The maids, to keep the elves aloof,
  Will bar the doors in vain;
No key-hole will he fairy-proof
  When green leaves come again.

THOMAS HAYNES BAYLY

Seeing Fairies

Many people claim to have seen fairies, but most of them – unfortunately – have turned out to be fakes. Famous photographs of fairies were taken in 1917 by two cousins – Elsie Wright and Frances Griffiths – at Cottingley Glen in Yorkshire. The pictures even convinced the writer, Sir Arthur Conan Doyle, that fairies existed.

In the 1980s, the sisters confessed that they had simply photographed pictures of fairies that they had cut out of books and pinned to the bushes with hat-pins. However, both maintained to the end that they had genuinely seen fairies and had used the photos to try to reproduce what they had witnessed.

One girl who provided more proof than most of seeing fairies was Anne Jeffries, who was born around 1625 at St Teath in Cornwall. She was fascinated by the idea of fairies. As a teenager, she spent many evenings looking for them under fern leaves and inside foxglove flowers.

In 1645, while working for a family named Pitt, she had a seizure in their garden and was ill for some time. When she recovered, she declared that she had been carried away by six little fairy men to a wonderful and magical land full of temples and palaces built of gold and silver, surrounded by marvellous gardens. As proof of her contact with the fairies, she cured Mrs Pitt of an illness by touching her. She also cured other people and developed the ability to foretell the future.

Although Anne only visited Fairyland once, she claimed the fairies went on visiting her and brought her food, so that she seldom had to eat human food. In 1647, she was imprisoned and denied food for over a year because she prophesied the victory of the Royalists in the English Civil War, which was raging at the time. But Anne continued in good health, perhaps living off the food brought to her by the fairies. Anne's story was published by Matthew Pitt, the son of her employers, in 1696 and is mentioned in other letters of the time.

I Believe

Fairies are elusive, wondrous little things,
We saw them best as children, tried to touch
their fairy wings.
But now that we are all grown up and adult,
we don't see,
Those tiny wonderous beings, that we saw
when we were three.
They visit us each morning flying round as
we get up,
The sleep that we wipe from our eyes, comes
from their fairy cup.
They wait and hope that we will say those
words they long to hear;
'I believe in Fairies', say it loud and
say it clear.
For every time you say it, another fairy
will survive,
But when you say 'I don't believe',
another fairy dies.

'I believe in Fairies!'

Felicia D. Browne-Hemans

A Spell to see Fairies

This spell is recorded in an ancient manuscript. It tells you how to make an ointment that will let you see the fairies.

❀ Gather the flowers of roses and marigolds while looking towards the east. Take the petals and soak them separately in spring water for one week. Strain off the petals.

❀ Pour a small quantity of each liquid into a crystal glass bowl.

❀ Add some virgin olive oil, and beat the mixture until the oil turns white. Then pour it into a glass bottle.

❀ Add hollyhock buds, marigold flowers, young hazel buds and the flowers of wild thyme to the mixture. The thyme should be gathered from the side of a hill 'where fairies used to go often'.

❀ Add grass from a fairy throne and leave the bottle in the sun for three days for the ingredients to dissolve.

❀ Rub a very little of the mixture on each eyelid and you will be able to see any fairies who are around.

This may have been some people's way to see fairies, but others say that all the fairies left Britain during the reign of Oliver Cromwell (1649–58), because they could not endure the Puritans (a group of very austere Christians) who abolished Christmas and other public holidays.

One tale from Sussex, dating from about Cromwell's time, tells how one band of fairies recruited two brothers – one blind and the other dumb – to take them out to sea. Perhaps the fairies boarded a ship going to America and never set foot in Britain again.

Ida Rentoul Outhwaite was born in Australia in 1888, the second surviving daughter of a presbyterian minister and professor at the University of Melbourne. The family had emigrated from Northern Ireland in the 1870s. Ida and her older sister Annie collaborated on a series of books and songbooks with Ida producing all the illustrations – the first one appeared in 1903. She also illustrated books for other authors and freelanced for newspapers and magazines.

In 1909, she married Grenbry Outhwaite who enthusiastically promoted her work and also wrote the text for some of her later books. In 1920, she visited England and held an exhibition of her work in Bond Street, London. This was a great success, and as a result, some of her books were also published in England by A. & C. Black. The last of her major books appeared in 1930, although she continued to illustrate music sheets and make the occasional painting for a book, up to her death in 1960.

Some of Ida's illustrations from the following books are reproduced here: *Australian Songs; Before the Lamps are Lit; Blossom; Bunny & Brownie; The Enchanted Forest; Fairyland; The Lady with the Blue Beads; The Little Fairy Sister;* and *The Little Green Road to Fairyland.*

© Copyright Buster Books, 2001
Illustrations © V & S Martin, 2001

First published in Great Britain in 2001 by Buster Books,
an imprint of Mary Ford Publications Ltd,
a subsidiary of Michael O'Mara Holdings,
9 Lion Yard, Tremadoc Road, London SW4 7NQ, UK.

ISBN 1–903840–19–8

Visit our website at www.mombooks.com

Compiled by Diana Briscoe
Jacket design by Robert Walster
Text designed and typeset by DW Design
Printed in Singapore.